Dr. Dave

Clark Sturges teaches English at Diablo Valley College in Pleasant Hill, California. His other books are *A Strategy for Writing, Witnesses*, and *Saying It Straight: Writing by Ordinary People.*

Dr. Dave

A Profile of David E. Smith, M.D.,
Founder of the Haight Ashbury Free Clinics

Clark S. Sturges

DEVIL MOUNTAIN BOOKS
Walnut Creek, California

Clark S. Sturges

Dr. Dave

A Profile of David E. Smith, M.D., Founder of the Haight Ashbury Free Clinics

DEVIL MOUNTAIN BOOKS, P.O. BOX 4115, WALNUT CREEK, CA 94596. ALL RIGHTS RESERVED.

Designer: Wayne Gallup

Typesetter: Susan Garcia / Imagery Designs

Copy editor: Jackie Pels

Photo consultant: Bruce Millar

Typestyle: Palatino

Library of Congress Cataloging-in-Publication Data

Sturges, Clark.
    Dr. Dave : A Profile of David E. Smith, M.D., Founder of the Haight Ashbury Free Clinics / Clark S. Sturges.
        p.   cm.
    ISBN 0-915685-08-6
    1. Smith, David E. (David Elvin), 1939-   . 2. Physicians—California—Biography. 3. Haight-Ashbury Free Medical Clinic.
    I. Title.
    R154.S519S88 1992
    610′.92—dc20
                                       92-54544
  [B]   CIP

123•76543

For Mom, Dad, and Ralph

CONTENTS

PREFACE

*T*wenty-five years ago, on June 7, 1967, David E. Smith, M.D., 28 years old, opened the Haight Ashbury Free Medical Clinic in San Francisco, the first of its kind in the United States and the catalyst for a free clinic movement that would become worldwide. Dr. Dave believed health care was a right, not a privilege, and that it should be free for all who need it. Two and a half decades later, the issue of free or affordable health care for all Americans was a major topic in the 1992 political campaigns.

The "free" meant much more to Dave than "no charge" and introduced a radical health-care philosophy emphasizing medical treatment free from red tape, free from value judgments, free from eligibility requirements, emotional hassles, frozen medical protocol, moralizing, and mystification. The clinic opened as a response to the medical needs of 100,000 young hippies who were descending on San Francisco for the Summer of Love. On that day in June, Dave wasn't sure the clinic would last the month, let alone the summer.

Today the clinic — actually a group of clinics — is alive and well to the surprise of everyone who was involved with the clinic in 1967. Along with primary care, the clinics focus on concerns such as chemical dependency, AIDS prevention and treatment, and women's health issues. In addition, they provide specialized services ranging from medical treatment at rock concerts to jail psychiatric services. Dr. David Smith, founder, president, and medical director, oversees an annual budget of more than $8 million and a staff of 500, including 200 paid employees. There are six major sections operating at 13 different sites in the San Francisco Bay Area.

David Smith, now 53, is a remarkably talented man. Along with his clinic responsibilities, he's research director of the MPI Treatment Services of Summit Medical Center in Oakland and is an associate professor of occupational health and clinical toxicology at the University of California Medical Center in San Francisco, his alma mater. He serves as a consultant to many healthcare agencies and has lectured to physicians, drug counselors, and psychologists in all 50 states and abroad in Hong Kong, the Philippines, England, France, Switzerland, Sweden, and Israel.

Even with all his travels he still has time to keep up on current research and to write. He has written more than 275 articles and 20 books. In addition, he holds approximately 10 editorial positions and belongs to a host of professional societies.

This is his story, written by someone who has known him for almost 40 years. David and I were classmates at East Bakersfield High School, and we've kept in touch, in varying degrees, ever since. Many life histories take some strange twists and turns. But Dave's revelations — intensely personal and honest — will probably be surprising even to many who know him.

He tells of years of loneliness and insecurity, especially during his time in school, and he admits to battles with alcohol and drugs. He now is 100 percent drugfree and has been since the '80s. A major part of his life, along with his unconditional devotion to his family, is his commitment to an anonymous 12-step self-help recovery program. He hopes this part of his story — his recovery and all the benefits that have resulted from it — will help others who suffer from addiction. To reveal so much of himself takes strength and confidence, both of which are characteristic of Dr. Dave.

Dr. Dave

A Profile of David E. Smith, M.D.,
Founder of the Haight Ashbury Free Clinics

The Valley Years

Boys at Play

*E*veryone who has driven through the southern San Joaquin Valley has a favorite Bakersfield story — the heat, the fog, the smog, the desolation. Those who have lived there, though, speak less of the physical environment and more of community and family — a good place to make friends and raise children, kids like David Smith.

He was born February 7, 1939, the son of Dorothy Hildegarde McGinnis Smith and Elvin William Smith, in a Bakersfield maternity hospital. Both parents had Oklahoma roots. Elvin's parents settled in Bakersfield in 1901 after leaving Oklahoma, and Elvin was born in 1909 in what was then a small valley town. After Dorothy's family lost their farm in the Dust Bowl Depression, they too migrated to the southern San Joaquin Valley, settling in Lindsay, near Bakersfield, in hopes of finding jobs in the fields and packing sheds.

Dorothy and Elvin were married in July of 1936. Dorothy was a nurse, thanks to her family who had worked overtime hours in the fields so she could attend nursing school. Elvin worked as a clerk for the Southern Pacific Railroad. The home in which David was raised — essentially his only one in Bakersfield — was a modest cottage at 2228 Oregon Street just two blocks from East Bakersfield High School, from which he would graduate in 1956. The neighborhood was pretty much middle-class, and the folks living there were electricians, carpenters, store employees, and teachers.

According to David, the most influential person in his life was his mother. When he was in first grade at Horace Mann Elementary School, the family learned to their dismay that Dorothy had Hodgkin's disease, a form of cancer that affects the lymph nodes. In the mid '40s this disease was often fatal — and quickly fatal. Initially her doctors in Los Angeles gave Dorothy just three months to live. This prognosis was devastating for David.

Nitrogen mustard treatments, a form of cancer chemotherapy new at the time, put the disease in remission, however, and before long she was able to return to work and resume her former routine as nurse, wife, and mother. For at least half of that school year, David lived with Elvin's sister, Evelyn Adam, who still resides in Bakersfield and who speaks fondly of David, recalling that he was an unusually well-behaved child. But his mother's "sickness," as he calls it, shaped the life of the family, which he describes as "very close-knit, loving, but surrounded by the aura of death." The adults knew that when Dorothy went to Los Angeles every three months for treatment, there was a chance she would not return.

After her illness struck, Dorothy decided to leave the hospital where she had worked and become a private-duty nurse. She worked nights caring for severely ill people, many of whom, according to Aunt Evelyn, were quite well-off. Presumably this job provided more income, which would help with the medical bills Dorothy knew would continue to mount up for the rest of her life.

With Elvin working during the day, and Dorothy sleeping during the day, life became lonely for David. Shortly before this time, a new family had moved in across the street at 2229 Oregon — the Bakers: Caroline, Lyle, and son, Larry, who was about the same age as David. The two boys had become friends, and the two families shared backyard cookouts and watched TV together — the Smiths had the first set on the block — for years.

Because Dorothy wanted the house quiet while she slept, David often played after school at Larry's. And because the Smiths didn't take many vacations —

partly because of Dorothy's job and partly because they wanted to save money for David's education — David went camping, fishing, and traveling with the Bakers. Caroline, who now lives in Petaluma, said David became part of the family and loved the freedom their family provided since his life at home was much more regimented than theirs.

The year before the onset of Dorothy's sickness, 1943, David and Larry had started school at Horace Mann, going to kindergarten together the first day. The main thing separating David from the other kids was his age — with a February birthday he was considerably younger than the others, in some cases by as much as a year.

Larry, now a Bay Area community college teacher and computer consultant, recalls that David was a real behavior problem at Horace Mann. He was part "clown and screw-up," "always restless," "disruptive," in short a handful for his teachers. Caroline Baker, an elementary teacher at another school, recalls some of David's teachers remarking about what a problem he was.

Neil Wilcox, a Horace Mann classmate of David's and now a middle-school teacher in Bakersfield, remembers pretty much the same thing. Neil attributes much of David's behavior — pinching, poking, talking out of turn — to immaturity and basic high energy. Neither Neil nor Larry can recall much about David's classroom performance, but at least he was passed along year after year with the rest of the kids.

David loved to participate in sports. Although no one could see much athletic talent in this small, pudgy kid, what mattered at that stage was energy, not skill. But after a football game in the fifth grade after school, David told his mother he felt exhausted and his side hurt. Dorothy, using her nursing skills, took a urine sample and found blood. Doctors discovered that he had a congenitally deformed kidney and operated to repair it. During his recovery he had a tube protruding from his side from which fluid drained into a bottle. David's buddies from Horace Mann remember that this didn't slow him down in the least, and they recall him playing games, riding bikes, and running, all the time holding onto his tube and bottle. He was determined not to miss out on the things that were important to him. *Determined.*

To David's playmates, Elvin Smith was pretty much in the background, and Dorothy was a nice, kind woman, though just one of the mothers. Caroline, Larry, and David agree that Dorothy was the dominant parent. As Caroline says, "Dorothy had plans — and David had to follow them whether he wanted to or not." David says she continually emphasized to him that because he was the only male child on either side of the family, it was up to him to succeed.

Given Dorothy's upbringing, this was not surprising. Her family, though poor, had emphasized personal initiative and believed that success would follow from education and hard work. Dorothy recounted stories of humiliation while working in the fields during the Depression with her mother and sisters. When the boss

David's first portrait

Elvin and Dorothy

Second Grade at Horace Mann
First row, Jimmy Hill; third row, David, Dennis DeWalt, and Bob
Pacina; fourth row, Larry Baker

David taking a shot

Practicing in the back yard

would ask her mother what kind of work she would do, she would tell him she would do anything. Dorothy told David never to say he would do anything, but instead to say he would do those things he was trained to do, to perform skills like those of a doctor. David Smith, as far as Dorothy was concerned, was going to do good things and be *somebody*.

Elvin Smith, whose father had worked for an oil company and whose early life had been much easier than Dorothy's, had hoped to become a railroad engineer. But when his wife became ill, he decided he didn't want a job that would take him away from her. Although he was never promoted beyond chief clerk for Southern Pacific, he was able to be home with his family every day.

After David's incision healed he experienced a growth spurt, and his general health improved. In 1950 he looked forward to Washington Junior High, where he hoped to play sports and maybe even get on a league team. In the classroom he had calmed down a bit, but he certainly wasn't earning a reputation as a scholar. Both Neil and Larry recall several junior high teachers telling David that he "wouldn't make it" and that the next hurdle, high school, "would do him in."

Shooting Hoops

His eighth-grade year proved to be a turning point for David. Many of his neighbors and school chums attended Trinity Methodist Church in East Bakersfield, and that year the church put together a basketball team as part of a local league. The four main players were Dennis DeWalt, Jimmy Hill, Neil Wilcox, and Jerry Urner — and then there were David Smith and some others. The coach had played basketball in the army, and he brought discipline to the game, which the boys hadn't experienced before.

All of a sudden David saw hope. He realized that good players were not necessarily great natural athletes like DeWalt and Wilcox, who later would letter 12 and 10 times respectively in high school, but that average players could become good ones by employing discipline and hard work, those qualities Dorothy had instilled in him. Dennis DeWalt now heads the DeWalt Corporation, a large civil engineering and land development company in Bakersfield. As he puts it, the Trinity team taught David how to be an athlete and how to overcome his awkwardness by "working 10 times harder than the others." That Trinity team competed for the league title and lost in overtime.

Jim Hill, a business officer for San Jose State University, recalls walking by David's house at dusk and seeing him practicing free throws using a crude hoop set up in his backyard, throwing the ball hour after hour. The backboard had come from a play yard in a vacant lot behind David's house. When the lot was sold, Vaughn Ward, a neighbor and athletic mentor to many of the neighborhood kids, had given the backboard to David. Practice time increased, and this began a work ethic that to this day dominates much of his academic, professional, and even social life.

When David entered East Bakersfield High School in 1952, he realized that his "squirreliness" in school would have to end, and he applied his free-throw ethic to all aspects of his life. When his high school chums recall him, the words "driven," "disciplined," "serious," and "competitive" come up with amazing frequency. He knew that to become *somebody* he would have to excel at academics, and additionally he hoped to achieve his personal goal of becoming an athlete. This road, however, would prove to be a rocky one.

As a freshman he was both young and small. When he enrolled he stood 5 foot 3 inches and weighed 105 pounds. Because of his size and past kidney problems, football was out of the question, but other sports were possible. He made the "D" basketball squad, which elated him. He tried out for baseball, probably his favorite sport, but his size was against him and he was cut, a major disappointment.

During this time, David, Dennis DeWalt, and Bill Thompson plus a few others earned some extra money by caddying at Bakersfield Country Club. Bill today lives in Bakersfield and is an electrical engineer working for A-C Electric Company. David became intrigued with golf and approached it with the same intensity and discipline he applied to everything else. In his compulsive, goal-oriented way, he began to practice incessantly and ultimately was able to shoot a good score. His frequent playing partner was Dennis DeWalt, who was the best golf player in high school. Later they entered a citywide tournament against country club kids.

Dennis won with a 73, and David placed second with a 78.

Dennis played baseball in the spring, so he wasn't a member of the school golf team. David, however, joined the golf squad his junior year, competed well, and earned his first varsity letter in this sport. Part of his success he attributes to another growth spurt. The increased height and weight helped him on the court as well as the links.

His whole life at this time became one of discipline. Larry Baker recalls that David told him that he was going to have to decide what things would be important in his life, and that he would have to incorporate those things into his schedule. David decided that reading a newspaper would be important, so he allocated 20 minutes a day to the newspaper — not 15 or 25, Larry says, but 20. Aunt Evelyn recalls the same kind of discipline at her home on Friday nights before a basketball game. David would eat dinner and then grab a textbook and read whatever homework had been assigned until he had to hop into his car and go to the gym or team bus.

The car! One of the things that stands out in David's mind today — and also in the minds of his high school friends — is the '47 Chevy he bought his junior year even before he was old enough to get his driver's license. The car had belonged to Vinton Sommerville, a varsity basketball player and all-around BMOC who was dating Maureen Mahoney, one of the cutest and most popular girls on campus. The car was maroon and lowered with twin chrome pipes and moon hubcaps. It was David's pride and joy, and it gave him prestige and a means to free himself from Oregon Street and expand his social horizons. David recalls getting up every morning and shoe-shining the pipes and then driving the two blocks to school at 5 miles an hour and cruising back and forth in front of the front lawn until his first class began.

From the beginning of high school David was an excellent student, always at the top of his class. His approach to school was typical: Set a goal, devise a plan of attack, follow through step by step to reach his objective. In the same way, he moved from "D" basketball through "C" and "B" to make the varsity team his senior year when, according to Dennis DeWalt, he had indeed become what he had always set his sights on, an accomplished athlete. Seemingly he had achieved it all.

Outsider

But in his eyes, at least, those years were troubled ones, not ones of achievement. He says today that he was full of insecurity and "distrusted happiness" because he expected things to go wrong just as they had in the past. His mother's sickness was always a presence in his home, and because of his working-class roots he felt that he didn't measure up to many of the other kids in school — that his family wasn't "good enough" and that he didn't have the social skills to allow him to become an insider. Forming good, positive relationships with girls was beginning to present itself as a problem too.

Buying the Chevy was a milestone as was his initiation into the A.V.S., a social group made up of nine boys at the high school. It came about completely spontaneously during the summer of 1954, before his junior year, when a few kids from the high school spent the night at one of the boy's houses when his parents were away. The evening consisted of roughhousing, storytelling, and probably beer drinking, and the boys hatched the idea that the next time there was a house available the same kind of party would take place.

It was a remarkable group, considering the context of the 1950s in an unsophisticated burg in the Central Valley. Of the nine, all graduated from college, five have advanced degrees, and two others are licensed engineers. Most interestingly, seven are still in close touch with one another and were in attendance at David's 50th birthday party in 1989 and at the wedding of Jim Hill's daughter, Karen, in 1991.

At the time, all of the members were either good at sports or active in student government or both. David remembers how thrilled he was to be invited to join, since he didn't feel he was on the same level as the other boys. No one else remembers it this way — David was one of the guys and seemed on a par with everyone else. In addition, the club really didn't have any formal admissions policy. The kids who hung out at the parties became members because of their presence, and when the number reached nine the group agreed that that was enough.

Varsity basketball, 1956
First row, left to right, Neil Wilcox, David Smith, Harold Clements,
Johnny Callison; second row, Dennis DeWalt, Richard Tucker, Chuck
Gunnerson, Jim Coffelt, David Jackson; third row, Raymond Bryant,
Ronnie Hamilton, Mr. Jim Waterman, Corney Morales, Jerry Urner,
Tim Hay

The '47 Chevy

**BAKERSFIELD
ACADEMY OF
VACUOUS SIPPERS**

A.V.S.　　**CHARTER
MEMBER**

"Down With Water"

This certifies that

David Smith

**Political
Immunity!**　　is a member in good standing

The process of "naming" the A.V.S. came about as a kind of prank. Jim Hill recalls initials were big in the mid-'50s and that someone came up with the name of Associated Vodka Sots, since most of the sleepovers involved some form of alcohol. Later, the name was refined to Academy of Vacuous Sippers, and the boys actually had membership cards printed up with a caricature of a little guy standing by a gigantic martini glass. The Senior Index in the 1956 *Sierran*, the high school yearbook, lists membership in the A.V.S. after the names of Tommy Alexander, Larry Baker, Dennis DeWalt, Jim Hill, Denny Ralph, Bill Thompson, David Smith, Clark Sturges, and Bill Weekes. The yearbook editor, part of the gang, slipped the identifications in behind the advisor's back.

As previously mentioned, drinking was part of the A.V.S. activities, and it took various forms. While certain behavior remains unremarkable, David Smith's does not. He approached drinking as he approached everything else: Establish a goal (get drunk), make a game plan (drink as much and as fast as you can), and attain the objective (get rowdy and probably pass out). "Social" drinking wasn't David's style, as he readily admits today. And as Neil Wilcox says, "David drank to get smasharooed."

David recalls problems at this time with his father's drinking. According to David, Elvin wasn't a binge drinker like Lyle Baker, Larry's father, but a quiet, steady drinker who went to work, came home, drank and then sometimes passed out on the couch. He never became abusive or argumentative but just "silly." The boys closest to the family at that time, Larry Baker and Jerry Urner, have no recollection at all of any drinking problem, and Larry flat-out denies that David's dad had one, at least to the extent that David has described.

One aspect of his life that David's high school friends remember more than any other is his behavior with girls. David admits and others concur that he never had a real girlfriend at East High and rarely participated in school parties or dances. Instead, he went out with girls who to this day mostly remain nameless. They were often younger, and most were girls who, in '50s parlance, were out to have a good time and liked to drink. What's important here isn't the nature or extent of David's sexual dalliances but rather the way he went about them. A very predictable way.

As Larry Baker puts it, "David would put his blinders on and work out a plan to get laid. He'd pick the girl, gas up the Chevy, stoke up on booze, and begin the campaign." David agrees pretty much with this interpretation but believes alcohol was the critical factor in terms of his behavior. When sober, he was shy and polite with girls, he says, but after drinking he underwent a major personality change, becoming aggressive and persistent.

Although some of the girls were from his high school, others were pickups on the streets. Bill Thompson recalls going to a Fats Domino concert with David, after which David spotted a girl he knew and they picked her up. After the concert, Bill says they took her home, and he was shocked to see that she lived in a house literally made of cardboard. He believes that many of the girls David found were looking for some way to get out of the life they were trapped in, and if sex might lead to a way out then so be it.

Why didn't a great student and competitive athlete date the popular girls? According to him, he didn't feel he was good enough, that his family was good enough. He believed his farmworker ancestry and working class upbringing didn't qualify him for the good girls.

One of the good girls, Loretta Templeton Nolthenius, a 1956 East High songleader who now lives in Alameda and works as an orthodontist's receptionist in San Leandro, remembers that indeed she had gone out with David to a Women's Club dance, she thinks between her sophomore and junior year, and she remembers having a good time — not a romantic time but just fun. She recalls that socially David was "just there" — not terribly athletic or articulate but also not the wildest. She said that had he asked her out again she thinks she would have gone because she wouldn't have had a reason not to.

Another songleader, Maureen Mahoney Hamilton, a registered nurse living in San Clemente and working in Laguna Beach, says she wouldn't have gone out with him because he wasn't part of the "in" crowd that she thought she was part of and that he was more of the "studious type." Neither Loretta nor Maureen mention any concern about his reputation with "bad" girls, but the men who grew up with him think this must have been a factor.

His senior year, however, David did take a date to the Junior-Senior Prom. She is Joan Papasergia Wallace, who still lives in Bakersfield, works part-time for the Department of Agriculture and is married to Art Wallace, a Superior Court judge. Joan was a senior at Garces Memorial High School, the Catholic school, and she says David was a fun guy, a perfect gentleman, and the evening was terrific.

Torment and Conflict

The diagnosis of Dorothy's cancer had been momentous, but her unexpected death in 1956 — unexpected to him, at least — was a stunning blow to David. Dorothy and Elvin had gone to LA for her routine nitrogen mustard treatments, and David was staying across the street with the Bakers. He remembers being in the bathroom getting ready for school when Lyle Baker walked in and said, "David, your mother's dead." He couldn't believe it. Later he learned that all his adult relatives were well-prepared for her death, and he raged at them for not telling him, for preparing him. But he recognizes now that in those times death was something that wasn't talked about, especially to youngsters.

Feeling helpless after the news, not knowing how to act, he pulled himself together and followed his regular routine and went to school. He kept his emotions under control for several days, continued to go to basketball practice, and the following Friday played one of his best games against rival Delano. According to Neil

Wilcox, their opponents were much better, but East High played a stall game and squeaked through with a victory.

The Delano players were furious and accosted David and his teammates in the parking lot after the game, and during a scuffle one of Delano's biggest boys, a kid named Barney, kicked in the moons on David's prized Chevy. David tried to stop him and was cold-cocked. No one was going to mess with his Chevy without a fight.

The following week he was called into Coach Jim Waterman's office to talk about the fight. At the end of the conversation, Coach Waterman told David softly that he knew about his mother's death and offered a few words of consolation. David burst into tears, letting out all the emotions he had kept inside. Jim Waterman, who later became principal at the high school and is now retired, still remembers the incident.

Jim also recalls that although David didn't have as much natural ability as some of the other boys, he became a fine basketball player, and his senior year he was the leading scorer on the varsity team. Jim volunteered two anecdotes about David's basketball abilities. The first involved free throws, for which there was a 10-second time limit. The coach remembers watching David wait, and wait, and wait, and thinking, "Will he ever get it off in time?" David would let it fly with about a half-second to spare.

The second was a game at Visalia when David was playing "B" ball. East High had just scored, but

Visalia did a poor job of in-bounding and the ball became loose. David snatched it off the floor, jumped, shot...swish. But into the wrong basket! Fortunately this didn't affect the game's outcome. Coach Waterman remembers saying to Coach Larry Laffond on the bus trip home, "How could someone with that brilliant a mind do something like that?"

Dorothy's early death committed David even more to fulfill her expectations — to be somebody. Dorothy had always had high regard for people in the health-care professions and had guided David toward dentistry because dentists were well-respected, made lots of money, and had secure jobs — and because the training was probably not as difficult as medical school. David believes that after Dorothy's death he began to assess his skills and interests and decided for himself that he did want to become a health-care professional — a *somebody*. But he thought medicine was a better goal for him. For one thing, he realized that his manual dexterity was not as good as his intellect. But he never wanted to be a doctor to "heal the sick." He wanted to become one for the financial security and social standing that would follow.

In June 1956 he graduated from East Bakersfield High School and made plans to attend Bakersfield Junior College. Other changes were ahead for him as well.

After Dorothy's death Elvin became depressed, cried frequently, and drank more heavily. David, too, began to drink more than he had previously, and he concluded later that both he and his father had exhibited "alcoholic drinking." In short, father and son drank to get drunk and did so a lot.

To cure his loneliness Elvin began to date, and in 1957 he married a spinster kindergarten teacher who had come to Bakersfield from the East Coast. During their courtship David and she had gotten along quite well, but after the marriage, that changed. Elvin's new wife wanted to be a mother to David, but he had had a mother he had loved deeply and didn't want another one. He rebelled against her attempts to control him, and the situation within the family became tense and unpleasant.

At this time the Smiths moved to a newer home near the college and rented out the Oregon Street house, which Elvin and his wife would return to when David left Bakersfield. The new surroundings didn't improve things. His wife began to tell Elvin what a rotten son David was, that he drank constantly and excessively and ran around with the town tramps.

Aunt Evelyn Adams thinks that David's stepmother was jealous of the relationship between Elvin and David and wanted to undermine it. Evelyn told her to stop trying to change a teenager and to "never say a word against your husband's child." David spent as little time as possible with his stepmother. During the summer he worked for the railroad in small valley towns like Huron and Delano, which kept him away from the house and put more distance between him and his father's marriage that had turned out to be a "complete disaster," a phrase used by both David and Aunt Evelyn.

In one sense, at least, Bakersfield College was disappointing. When students leave high school communities to attend commuter schools, which most junior colleges are, their former social groups tend to disintegrate. This happened to David, and it bothered him intensely. Several of the boys in his gang had gone away to four-year schools, and others had steady girlfriends they spent their spare time with. Those at the junior college had different schedules — and most weren't math-science students as David was, so they didn't take the same classes. The social acceptance that David had begun to feel in high school disappeared, and he began to hang out with a variety of different groups. But the connections with them were far more casual than what he had had before and more casual than what he now wanted.

His carousing continued and probably the apex occurred during spring break in 1957 when David and a bunch of junior college kids — not the friends from East High — started drinking and decided to go to the Long Beach Pike, a big amusement park frequented by sailors and local toughs. Full of booze they all got tattoos inked on their right calves, convinced that macho guys who were good at sports and good at getting girls had tattoos. David's is a heart with a dagger through it and the word "Dave."

In June of 1958 he graduated from Bakersfield Junior College with an Associate in Arts degree and high academic honors, packed up the '47 Chevy, and headed to Berkeley and the university to do whatever it would take to be *somebody*.

The Bay Area:
A New Home

Culture Clash — The Berkeley Years

*H*is introduction to Berkeley was terrifying. The first thing Dave Smith noticed was that no other car he saw was like his maroon pride and joy: no pipes, no lowered suspensions, no tucked and rolled upholstery. And the whole scene was completely different from home in Bakersfield — Berkeley was cosmopolitan, sophisticated, progressive. He felt like a real hick. What was he doing here? What had he gotten himself into?

His first residence was in a flat in North Berkeley, where he shared a bedroom with a Bakersfield buddy, Bob Pacina, whose friendship went all the way back to Horace Mann Elementary School and through high school and junior college. Bob's major was music and Dave's was pre-med, or at least that's what Dave recalls. Bob, who now lives in Eugene, Oregon, and is a respiratory therapist, believes that Dave was still planning to attend dental school and remembers him preparing for a digital dexterity test, which was part of the dental school's entrance requirements. Larry Baker, who had transferred from Bakersfield College to San Jose State, remembers the same chronology. In any event, whether dentistry or medicine, Dave Smith was following his plan of becoming a health-care professional.

Bob remembers that Dave was a serious student, that he had a girl friend, he thinks, and that Dave's academic and social habits were pretty much like those of all the other students who were trying to adjust to a new climate. He says the two of them kept a jug of cheap red wine handy but doesn't recall any excessive drinking — or anything more excessive than what other kids in their late teens and away from home for the first time were doing.

Dave was as terrified of the rigors of school as he was of the worldliness of Berkeley, and he was afraid he didn't belong in either place. He decided that he would have to apply himself to the limit if he were going to live up to Dorothy's expectations. He studied harder than he ever had and it paid off — straight A's his first semester. While that increased his confidence a little, there still were nagging fears telling him that he wasn't good enough and that he would fail.

When Dave entered the university he knew almost nothing about the culture he now was a part of. He didn't even know what a fraternity was. But true to his nature he gathered as much information as he could and learned that fraternities had good parties and that often the cutest girls liked to go out with frat boys. So he decided to enter the Greek rush and later that term pledged Alpha Tau Omega.

Although Bob Pacina hadn't observed it, Dave recalls that his drinking patterns were pretty much what they had been in high school and junior college — sober for a while, then sprees of excessive drinking and drunkenness. He remembers having a "remarkable capacity for screwing up relationships, getting drunk and messing up." He seemed to develop a pattern of dating a few girls he really cared about — and quite a few he didn't but had fun with — and then after drinking doing things that would turn away the girls he liked.

The larger Berkeley world, too, was one he was having trouble relating to. The social revolution of the '60s was beginning, and "Berkeley was becoming politically radical at a fundamental level," he recalls. But he didn't understand it, at least at first, and he didn't like what he was observing and didn't want to become part of it.

He remembers a discussion section leader, a graduate assistant, announcing passionately that he was canceling class that day and was going to take everyone to San Francisco for a political protest. Dave said that he didn't want to go, that he wanted to stay and study so he would get an A. The TA told him that if he *didn't* go he definitely *wouldn't* get an A!

But the new political philosophy was pervasive, and Dave began to think more and more about what was going on. The kid from the Valley read *The Grapes of Wrath* for the first time when he took a literature class at Berkeley. He thought hard about the social issues, the class struggles Steinbeck describes, and he realized he had grown up accepting prejudice as a Bakersfield reality. He recognized too that he was ashamed of his Okie background, which he believed had excluded him from belonging to the "right" levels of society.

So the strident moves to strike down prejudice and inequality began to make a lot of sense to him, and he began to hang out in Northside coffee houses where kids talked about existentialism and social change. He became part of the scene as a follower, not a leader, and he believes he identified with the movement because what was being called into question had been part of his upbringing, a part that had affected him negatively, and the sense of inadequacy created by this was still with him.

Across the Bay the beatnik scene was under way, and this fascinated him, too, though he observed it from a distance. He had gone with a girl in Bakersfield who had been sexually molested by her father and wanted out of her abusive environment. She had told Dave she wanted to move to San Francisco to become a beatnik, and he hadn't had the foggiest notion what she meant. Once in the Bay Area, however, he began to get a sense of the beat lifestyle, and her quest became clearer.

The second semester of his junior year he moved into the ATO house, where he lived until he graduated. The fall of his senior year, three of his Bakersfield buddies, Dean Challes, Phil Newlin, and Jerry Urner, came through the house — and they all pledged. Phil became Dave's roommate the second semester of his senior year.

Along with others, Phil Newlin remembers Dave as being serious and highly motivated. But according to Phil, "He always had time under a carefully organized schedule to play basketball and date lewd women." Dave was interested in ATO parties and sporting events but had little time for fraternity rituals, which he found superficial. Phil says that Dave was a good, careful listener, which many of the boys found appealing, but that by and large he "was different from the rest of the guys — kind of an outsider." Phil doesn't recall that Dave drank much differently than the other boys or at least much differently than he did.

Regarding Dave's social skills, Phil, who presently works for the California Department of Corrections as a contract negotiator, tells a story that illustrates one aspect of Dave Smith. Jim Mercer was a Berkeley ATO and a roommate of Phil's before he roomed with Dave. After graduation Mercer accepted a job on the East Coast. On a visit to San Francisco some 20 years later, he was walking in front of the medical school when he ran into his old buddy. Mercer shouted, "Dave Smith, son-of-a-bitch, how the hell are ya!" Smith looked up, said, "Oh, hi, Merce," and walked on. Clearly Dr. Dave had something else on his mind.

Neil Wilcox tells an almost identical story about East Bakersfield High School's 20th reunion in 1976. Neil hadn't seen Dave for a number of years and was excited when he heard he would attend. At a cocktail pre-party he spotted Dave across the room reading the 1956 yearbook. Neil shoved his way through the crowd to meet Dave, who gave him a quick look, said "Hi, Neil," then resumed reading.

Entering his senior year at Berkeley, Dave continued to study hard. Jerry Jorgensen, now a plastic surgeon in San Luis Obispo, did not know Dave well as an undergraduate, but he remembers that they were classmates in an embryology course, where success was essential if you hoped to make it to medical school. Jerry, sitting in the back of the room, noticed a student in the front row taking notes furiously and pumping his hand in the air asking questions of the professor. Jerry thought to himself, "Who is that jerk? He's going to screw up the curve." The jerk, of course, was Dave Smith.

But while he was succeeding in school by all conventional standards, he felt that "things weren't working." Inside him there was still something missing. And then personal tragedy struck again.

Elvin Smith had suffered from ulcerative colitis for a number of years, and in late 1959 his health began to fail. The loss of Dorothy and the accelerated drinking that followed her death were taking its toll. In December Elvin was hospitalized at the Southern Pacific Hospital in San Francisco, and in January of 1960 he died at the age of 51 from colitis complicated by liver failure.

Dave told Phil Newlin, "I'm all alone," and in many respects he was. At 20 he had lost both his mother and father, didn't have any brothers or sisters, and was left with a stepmother he detested.

The last time he saw Elvin's widow was at Elvin's funeral. Any chance of harmony between them ended when she challenged Dave's inheritance of the Oregon Street house. The house had been her residence, so she hired an attorney who argued in court that she should be given title to it under a homestead provision. The court agreed, and Dave was angry and resentful. He harbored these feelings for years, putting the bitterness aside only when his friend Dennis DeWalt convinced him that there wasn't much value in the property and that he should "let it go" in every sense of the word.

Dave's relatives knew how he felt about his stepmother, and he says that later in his life he reconciled his feelings towards her because his family kept emphasizing to him that she had been at Elvin's side when he died. But Aunt Evelyn Adam says that after Elvin's death Dave's stepmother petitioned the court to gain compensation for the hours she had spent caring for him in the hospital.

Dave decided his father's '56 Oldsmobile was a better car for him now, so he sold the Chevy to former roommate Bob Pacina and set his sights on medical school. He took the qualifying tests and completed his admission application — the only one he submitted anywhere — to UC San Francisco. He had heard that UC took care of its own, and with his high scores and good grades he didn't anticipate any problem getting in. And he was right — he did get in. But even with this success his insecurity remained.

San Francisco and the Haight

Dave's first home in San Francisco was Nu Sigma Nu, a medical fraternity located near the medical center. He lived there his first year and for most of his second, and then moved to St. Mary's Hospital with two classmates to work as externs helping with physical exams. He found medical school brutal. It wasn't the work that was overwhelming but the competition. All the students there had been at the top of both high school and college classes, and they battled each other for top grades. Dave did reasonably well, placing near the middle of his class or sometimes even a little higher, but the experience wasn't what he had expected, and he considered dropping out.

Giving up was not his way of responding to challenges, however. He thought things through and decided he needed to try something else along with medical school. In 1962 he enrolled concurrently in graduate school at the medical center to begin a course of study in pharmacology. He devoted all his elective time from his medical studies to pharmacology, with particular emphasis on psycho-pharmacology, which was a relatively new specialty and which he found much more exciting than medical school. Inspired by brilliant professors, he developed a clinical fascination for drugs.

Of course it wasn't all lab and library grind. For recreation Dave and some of the other graduate students would steal pure grain alcohol from the labs and make a punch guaranteed to create a monster party. Larry Baker elaborated a little about this, remembering that on occasion these parties — often folk music hootenannies — were advertised in the community. The sponsors made a little money, Larry recalls, and the party-goers, most of whom were minors, all got very drunk. Considering the risks involved, it was a dumb thing to do, but college students often do dumb things.

In 1964 Dave Smith graduated with his medical degree along with an M.S. in pharmacology. He interned at San Francisco General Hospital and from 1965 to 1967 worked as a post-doctoral fellow at the medical center in pharmacology and toxicology. In addition, he was chief of the Alcohol and Drug Abuse Screening Unit at San Francisco General. These were productive years for him professionally, but his personal life continued to be plagued by poor decisions, poor relationships, and destructive bouts with alcohol. He found he was falling into some disturbing patterns. He would have a disastrous evening and the next morning would vow never to lose control again. Then before long — maybe even the next night — he would drink again and screw things up even more.

Much of his carousing took place at The Transaction, a rock 'n' roll dance joint on Irving Street that he invested a little money in. Lee Grunden, a former classmate and now a pharmacology professor at the Pacific College of Osteopathic Medicine in Pomona, recalls that

David, a serious and directed scholar during the day, hung out there often, drinking and dancing with lots of different girls.

New Year's Eve, 1965, stands out vividly in Dave's mind. Earlier that year he had fallen in love, not for the first time, and he and his girlfriend began an intimate relationship that resulted in her becoming pregnant. Dave wanted her to have the child, but she wasn't sure about his stability and told him she would have to think about it. During the Christmas holidays she went home to be with her family.

Dave went to a New Year's Eve party alone, drank heavily, picked up a girl and later that evening picked up a second one, creating a tense situation for all three — and the second girl's abandoned boyfriend. When the story got back to Dave's girlfriend, he apologized and explained that he had suffered an alcoholic blackout, but she decided she couldn't take chances with his unreliability and had the abortion. This was an extremely emotional and troubling event for him.

With the awful New Year's Eve party and its consequences in mind, Dave attended a 12-step self-help recovery meeting and a Synanon session. Both groups were dealing with addiction but with different approaches. The 12-step approach had a spiritual foundation; Synanon was more confrontational. In 1966 Dave wasn't ready for either.

Soon after this he stopped drinking and began experimenting with psychedelics — marijuana, LSD, mescaline, ibogaine — and he liked the effects from them: expanded consciousness with no hangover and no guilt. Alcohol took a back seat to the drugs of the flower children.

At a party in 1966, Dave met a woman who would prove to be a tremendous influence in the new directions his life was about to take. Alice deSwarte was a committed hippie with counterculture values including a strong sense of social consciousness. Her lifestyle and values stood in stark contrast to the upper-class lives of the Ellis family into which Dave had almost married only four years before. Whether he knew it or not, that period in his life, 1961 - 1962, had paved the way for his meeting with Alice.

In 1961 Jennifer Ellis had graduated from Berkeley and was studying physical therapy at the medical center. She was everything Dave could ever hope for — beautiful, smart, and as in love with him as he was with her. Jennifer came from a wealthy and socially prominent Southern California family; her father was a successful and well-respected ophthalmologist. She and Dave became engaged in 1962.

Dave recalls the Ellises were very nice to him but that their world was entirely different from his. During his first visit they were all sitting around the backyard pool when Dr. Ellis noticed Dave's tattoo. A bit later he called Dave into his study and told him he would have to have it removed, that "we don't do those kinds of things in our family." Dave told him he had indeed thought of having it removed, but that it was part of his past and he had ambivalent feelings about it. The matter was left unresolved.

The Ellises gave elaborate parties for the couple, but with their family and friends only, not his. This added significantly to the loneliness he already felt. At one time there was even talk of Dave moving away from his friends in the Bay Area to Southern California to practice and perhaps to take up quarters in Dr. Ellis' medical building.

In a very real sense David Smith had found what he had been striving for all his life: A beautiful, nice girl who wanted to marry him, a wealthy family that would embrace him and help him establish a medical practice that would lead to financial security and membership in the right social and civic clubs. In short, he would fulfill Dorothy's dream — David Smith would be *somebody*.

He should have been the happiest man alive, but he wasn't. He began to realize that the relationship with Jennifer simply wouldn't work. He still can't say why, but he knew that things just didn't feel right. His dream come true wasn't making him happy. So he tearfully broke off the engagement, to Jennifer's dismay, and returned to school.

Jennifer Ellis McIntosh lives today in Pacific Palisades with her husband and two sons and teaches science part-time in local elementary schools. She and Dave remain friends and still communicate on occasion. She remembers vividly her first date with him. She and a girlfriend, Jan, were talking during a break in school when Dave walked by. Jan turned to Jennifer and said, "See that guy in the lab coat? I'm going out with him tonight." Jennifer, startled, said, "So am I!" They asked

Dave what was going on, and he confessed with embarrassment that he didn't remember making *two* dates. He proposed that he go with Jennifer and a buddy of his take Jan, and they all would go dancing. They did and all four had a good time, Jennifer recalls.

Dave and Jennifer both remember that Dave was searching for a family and for "conventionality." Jennifer was looking for just the opposite, and she found Dave off-beat and more interesting than the boys she had been dating. She believes today that Dave was right in ending the relationship. She thinks she was too young and not ready to make the break from her parents' influence and their expectations. She remembers Dave fondly as being open and honest — almost vulnerable — in his friendships. She feels he was empathetic with the little guy, and she can't see him following in her father's footsteps.

After breaking off his engagement to Jennifer, Dave was more alone than ever. In 1964 he tried to join the Air Force as a flight surgeon because of the training and benefits — a real "establishment" move. He was rejected because of his impaired kidney, and at the time that rejection was a major disappointment. Two years later, after meeting Alice deSwarte, he was marching in anti-war demonstrations!

Alice and Dave's first conversation was about LSD, a drug she had been studying. Dave had by this time experimented with LSD, so they talked about the nature of this popular psychedelic. Alice was studying education at San Francisco State College with the goal of becoming a special education teacher, a goal she later attained.

Alice was from an educated, middle-class family in Illinois who believed in using education to help others. This white, middle-class, spiritual girl, as she characterized herself, came west because she was attracted to the beat philosophy and lifestyle, which she found appealing because of its humor and sense of theater. She believed in radical social change with an emphasis on enlightening people spiritually as well as intellectually, and she talked persuasively to Dave about this.

Alice and Dave also talked about the Haight and the changes they were witnessing. The place was rapidly becoming a white teenage ghetto, and drug use was rampant. The word was out that the following summer as many as 100,000 kids from all over the country would find their way to the Haight to heighten their collective consciousness — aided, of course, by truckloads of mind-expanding drugs. It would be the Summer of Love, and David Smith's life would be changed forever.

Love Needs Care

Healing the Hippies

On January 14, 1967, the first Human Be-In was held in Golden Gate Park. Some 30,000 hippies (coined from Norman Mailer's "hipster") wearing beards, love beads, peace paint, psychedelic costumes — and sometimes nothing — gathered to celebrate joy and love and rock 'n' roll. Most were stoned.

Across the country the media flashed images of these kids laughing and dancing, and soon teenagers from Cedar Rapids and Cincinnati and Lubbock let it be known that come summer they would flock to San Francisco and the Haight to stage a counter-culture revolt and immerse themselves in sex, drugs, and music.

The city government was not amused. Mayor John Shelley issued an edict warning outsiders they would not be welcome and that if they came he would boost the police garrisons in the Haight. An ugly clash looked imminent.

At the time, besides serving as chief of the Alcohol and Drug Abuse Screening Unit at San Francisco General and completing his UC post-doctoral fellowship in pharmacology and toxicology, Dave Smith was participating in a psychopharmacology study group, also at UC, supervised by Dr. Frederick Myers. These students — medical doctors and pharmacologists — were focusing intently on the nature of psychedelics, and Dave recalls shooting drugs into his white mice during the day and then, as he walked home, seeing kids on the streets using the same drugs.

These medical scholars, as well as others in the community, became increasingly nervous about what emergency medical care would be available if and when the predicted 100,000 would-be hippies invaded the Haight in June. The city had said consistently that people who were sick would have to use the existing medical facilities, which already had demonstrated hostility toward the "dope fiends" who were then asking for treatment. City officials indicated that any problem was probably more criminal than medical and that more police action would be the remedy.

As a result, there began to be talk about establishing some sort of health center in the Haight that would deal with the bad effects of psychedelic drug use and the health problems endemic to communal living and general uncleanliness. But the form it would take was unclear.

At the time Dave was dating an African American nurse at the medical center, Florence Martin, who told him about a medical facility in Watts she had worked in which had been established to meet the needs of poverty-stricken patients after the riots of 1965. It also served as a neighborhood center with political influence, and Dave liked that notion.

Another model had existed during the civil rights marches in the South, where the protesters had taken with them their own medical units since, as Dave says, "There was the sense that if they had to go into a Southern hospital they might never come out."

Robert Conrich, a San Francisco architect's son, who had dropped out of the mainstream after taking LSD, had a vision of establishing a privately financed medical facility administered by himself, and he approached 27-year-old Dave Smith about running the medical side. Dave envisioned something like the Watts clinic, and he said he was interested.

The two began working together, but quickly the obstacles before them — permits, inspections, other rules and regulations — seemed overwhelming. But it occurred to them that if Dave were willing to put his reputation and license on the line, something might be worked out. On May 13, 1967, Dave set up a conference at the medical center to explore the possibilities. He and Robert Conrich had found an empty dentist's office at 558 Clayton at the corner of Haight, and they could open a clinic under the auspices of D.E. Smith, M.D., and Associates doing business as the Haight Ashbury Free Medical Clinic. The "associates" would be volunteers from the health-care community and from the Haight. People at the conference liked the idea.

On June 3 a meeting was held to see who the staff would be — essentially a meeting to find out who would show up. And the volunteers arrived, a motley group of health professionals and street people with at least one thing in common: a belief that health care is a right, not a privilege, and that it should be free to all who need it. The group decided on an opening date, June 7, 1967. The clinic would be financed by donations of money and contributions of supplies from companies and hospitals. Dave Smith paid the lease deposit out of his own pocket.

Today Dave shakes his head as he talks about it, saying it was "a crazy, insane thing to do considering the risks — I could have been wiped out financially for the rest of my life." But it was the '60s and the kids needed care.

June 7 arrived and no one knew exactly what to expect. What occurred, however, was both surprising and rewarding. Before the doors opened about 50 patients were already in line. Before the doors closed some 250 people had received medical treatment. It was a historic day, the beginning of the first free medical clinic of its type in the United States.

As reported in a history of the clinic's first 20 years, Dave Smith recalls the first day vividly: "Two things distinguished the line leading into the clinic that afternoon and evening — its diversity and its length. Most of the prospective patients strung around the corner of Haight and Clayton were young flower children and beats and older hippies wearing beads and buckskins who had not seen physicians in months.

"Some came with their commune-mates, made music together, and passed out flowers. Others stood quietly, cradling infants to their breasts. Several dozen patients were spilling into the hallway, lining up outside the single toilet or drinking water from the bathroom sink. It was a madhouse. And it was an exciting day!"

As patients trekked up the stairs to the intake room, they saw this sign and the clinic's logo, a white dove on a blue cross:

NO DEALING * NO HOLDING
NO USING DOPE * NO PETS
ANY OF THESE CAN
CLOSE THE CLINIC
WE LOVE YOU

The Haight Ashbury Free Medical Clinic was in business, but how long it would last would be a frequently asked question.

It's important to understand that the clinic wasn't an ambulance and tent sent from the medical center ready to be recalled. It was part of the fabric of nothing less than a counter-culture revolution calling for a reform of basic institutions, and there was a diversity of major players.

The Hell's Angels, who liked the hippies and liked doing drugs with them, became the justice system. The Diggers, named after a 17th century group of farmers who practiced utopian communism and considered private property the root of all social ills, operated soup kitchens and free stores. The beaded and flowered longhairs, though not organized, were a major presence, and HALO, the Haight Ashbury Legal Organization, gave free legal advice to anyone who had been busted. The Haight Ashbury Free Medical Clinc rounded this out as an institution advocating radical change in health-care delivery in the context of the most intense period of drug experimentation in the nation's history.

Another important consideration is the notion of "free," which has been part of Dave Smith's philosophy from the beginning. "Free" refers more to a state of mind than to the absence of a cashier, he says. A physician's focus should be on caring for the whole person and on providing a service that is free of charge but also free from red tape, free from value judgments, free from eligibility requirements, emotional hassles, frozen medical protocol, moralizing, and mystification. It was and is a revolutionary position.

Why did Dave Smith become a rebel? What happened to his ambition of becoming a mainstream doctor with all the trappings of success? Why would he invite the ridicule that would inevitably crop up? "David, where did you go wrong? You had such a promising career before you," a former medical professor told him in dismay.

A curious thing had happened to Dave Smith. He had always been an outsider — no family, no strong relationships that worked, a general sense of not belonging. In the summer of 1967 all that changed: For the first time in his life he felt he had become an *insider*. He had found a group of kids with many of the same insecurities and alienations he had recognized in his own life and he understood them. And he believed he had the knowledge, talent, and strength to administer a program that would put his newly realized philosophy into action. Dave Smith had found a home.

A Clinic Founded on Rock 'n' Roll

Money was a problem from the beginning, and one of the best things that happened to the clinic in its early days was an article written by a young reporter for the *San Francisco Chronicle,* David Perlman. Published on June 9, 1967, two days after the clinic opened, titled "A Medical Mission in the Haight-Ashbury," Perlman's story casts the work of Dave Smith and his volunteers in a very positive light. He first describes the scene: "With its bilious Victorian green walls and sparse furniture, the clinic could be any pad in the Haight-Ashbury. A radio plays rock music. A coffee pot steams. Kids, the boys mostly bearded, squat on the floor; many are stoned — turned inward to their private layers of drug-impaired consciousness.

"The girls look particularly frightened; some are very young, runaways perhaps; many have come with vaginal infections, and fear far worse. An occasional older alcoholic stumbles in, cut and bruised."

Later Perlman quotes Dr. Smith: "The surveys talk about the incidence of drug use among young people — 20 percent, they say, use marijuana; 5 percent use LSD.

"Here the figure is 100 percent. I haven't seen a kid in the clinic who hasn't used drugs, and most are using them right now. Marijuana, methedrine, DMT, LSD, and now the new one, STP.

"We want to tackle the drug problem here now. Not just by helping the kids come down from a bad trip, but by recruiting volunteer psychologists and psychiatrists for a serious after-care program that will follow up every patient. We'll do it if we get the volunteers."

Shortly after the article appeared, *Chronicle* columnists gave their support to the clinic and its programs. Herb Caen, Art Hoppe, Charles McCabe, and Ralph Gleason all wrote glowing items, and the money began to come in and volunteers began to show up. Kathy Grant Crosby came from her Hillsborough mansion to volunteer her nursing skills for three nights running. Hume Cronyn and Jessica Tandy came in after their stage show to volunteer in any way they could and when the night was over left a generous donation. Another major donation followed from TV personality Bonnie Franklin. Although the clinic and the city administration have had their ups and downs over the years, Dave

Honor society, UC Berkeley, 1960
First row, far right, Phil Newlin and Dave Smith

Young Dr. Dave listening and learning during the Summer of Love

Bill Graham
1931 - 1991

Part of the '70s scene

Dave, Cecil Williams, and Ruth Carter Stapleton at Glide Memorial Church

Smith says the San Francisco media have been consistently helpful and that the clinic wouldn't have made it without this support.

After Perlman's article, Dave received a call from Bill Graham, whom Smith knew about but had never met. Bill said he was interested in learning more about the clinic — that it sounded like good things were happening — so Dave invited him to 558 Clayton to see for himself. Bill Graham was the former office manager for Allis-Chalmers and a former producer of the radical San Francisco Mime Troupe. He had started to put together concerts and light shows at the Fillmore Auditorium and was fast becoming the P.T. Barnum of rock 'n' roll.

Bill, an intense Jewish orphan of the Holocaust, liked what he saw at the clinic and promised Dave that he would arrange some benefits to help pay the bills. That began a deep professional and personal friendship that lasted until Bill's tragic death in a helicopter accident on October 25, 1991. In the December 1991 issue of the clinic's newsletter, Dave Smith paid tribute to Bill Graham. Here are a few excerpts:

"Without Bill Graham, the clinic would not have survived its fragile infancy in the Summer of Love.... Bill donated his staff and the Fillmore Auditorium for a benefit concert on July 13, 1967. The Charlatans, Blue Cheer, and Big Brother and the Holding Company [with Janis Joplin] played — many of the bands' members were clinic patients. Over 2,000 people came to that concert, and we received $5,000, a monumental sum in those days.

"In 1970, Bill organized a Creedence Clearwater Revival benefit to help us start the Detox program. In 1974, the incredible George Harrison and Ravi Shankar concert helped us expand to 1696 Haight.

"Bill's favorite program was Rock Medicine. In the spring of 1973, he staged two consecutive Saturday concerts at Kezar Stadium featuring The Grateful Dead and Led Zeppelin. He asked us to staff a `medical emergency care tent' during both concerts — about 18,000 at the Dead and 25,000 at Led Zeppelin .... The `medical emergency care tent' became Rock Medicine.

"Bill Graham and the clinic thus pioneered a concept still not fully recognized — event medicine. Bill always felt that patrons at his concerts were his guests who should be provided with good entertainment in clean, safe surroundings. If they were hurt or sick, he had Rock Medicine on hand to provide medical care and psychological reassurance. Even his performers, security, production staff, and the concert halls' employees have come to rely on Rock Medicine's volunteers. Returning the patient to his family and friends as quickly as possible, minimizing the need for hospitalization or law enforcement, has been the watchword."

When Dave Smith accepted the Arthur M. Sohcot Award on behalf of the Haight Ashbury Free Clinics at the 1992 Bammies on March 7, 1992, he again memorialized Bill and called him the "patron saint" of the clinic. Bill Graham loved his family, Dave said, and the clinics were part of his extended family. The Sohcot Award salutes a group or individual who, through excellence in performance and/or professional activity, or through dedicated public service, has contributed to the betterment of the local community. Bill Graham Presents won the award in 1989.

Bill would have appreciated a letter Dave received in August 1992 from Jon J. Exworthy of San Francisco. It reads in part:

"Not long ago I had the good luck to obtain a ticket to a concert at Shoreline Amphitheater. On the way to this event I started to feel a little queasy, but I did not consider it very important.... By the end of the first set I was feeling quite ill. My girlfriend called Rock Medicine and they quickly put me in a wheelchair and rolled me down to the medical tent.

"Dr. Dave came over and felt around my stomach, asked a bunch of questions, and told me to get to a hospital immediately.... The doctors there confirmed what Dr. Dave had feared — I had acute pancreatitis. They told me that it was indeed a life-threatening situation, but because of early intervention I was spared permanent damage and was able to leave the hospital in just a week....Rock Medicine has saved my life, and I will always be grateful."

Although the Haight Ashbury Free Medical Clinic specifies *medical* care, almost from the beginning the clinics began to diversify. The Women's Needs and Detoxification sections were early expansions, and Dave Smith emphasizes that Bill Graham and his benefits were directly responsible for most of the expansions of the clinics.

Alice deSwarte was another major influence on Dave, especially in the early years. According to Dave, "Alice played a pivotal role in founding the clinic." After their first meeting in 1966, when Alice began to talk with Dave about radical social change, they developed a close relationship, and they were living together in the Haight when the clinic opened 1n 1967.

Alice became Dave's executive secretary, planner and organizer, and social arranger. She recalls that their home was often filled with junkies, drug dealers, lawyers, and musicians — leaders of the counter-culture revolution — and she remembers fixing hundreds of meals on the spur of the moment. During her lunch hour at San Francisco State, where she was doing graduate work in education, she made dittos of intake forms for the clinic, and at home she took care of much of the clinic's other paperwork. Later, when Dave began to publish extensively and started the *Journal of Psychedelic Drugs*, she did most of the final manuscript typing. She says today that Dave was the only health-care professional at the time who had the knowledge and temperament to treat the "acid freaks," and she supported his efforts 100 percent.

Alice, who married Dave in 1970 at the Unitarian Church in San Francisco, now lives with their daughters, Julia and Suzanne, in a small cooperative community in Sebastopol. Located there is the Smith Family Foundation headed by Richard Frank, who with his family is part of the community. The foundation supports innovative programs in art, education, and a recovery house for employed addicts called Plaza House. One of the programs is the Sebastopol Peace Garden, which Alice works on with Art Lisch, one of the original Diggers from the Haight.

Alice also teaches part time at a country preschool, and she and Dave are close friends and are still partners in real-estate investments they made during their marriage. When the girls aren't with Alice, they spend a lot of time with Dave, his wife, Millicent Buxton, and their son, Christopher, at their Victorian home in the Haight and at shows, ball games, and concerts their dad takes them to.

The Haight in the late '60s was a crazy scene. As Robin Williams says, "If you remember the '60s you weren't there." And a letter to the editor of the *San Francisco Chronicle* in March of 1992, shortly after Bill Clinton revealed that he had experimented with marijuana in England while a Rhodes Scholar, commented that anyone who was alive in the '60s and *hadn't* experimented with marijuana should be prohibited from holding public office because of being out of touch. But it wasn't all frivolity, and some scary things did go on.

Papa Al was a hanger-on close to the drug scene who had some run-ins with Dave about the operation of the clinic and about unfounded rumors regarding drug money going to the clinic. After a confrontation with Papa Al, Dave learned that a contract was out on his life and on the life of clinic administrator Don Reddick. Immediately, Don bought a handgun and shoulder holster for Dave, who recalls that his only experience shooting a gun was firing at bottles on the banks of the Kern River outside of Bakersfield. Dave called the police, who told him that they couldn't do anything until Papa Al acted. Dave told them that Papa Al's "act" would be to blow him away!

Several of Dave's advisors suggested that he call the Hell's Angels, so he put in a call to Sonny Barger, the Angels' leader at the time, whom he'd never met. Dave explained the threat on his life, and Sonny told him not to worry, that he would take care of things. As the story goes, the Angels went to Papa Al and told him that if anything happened to Dave Smith or Don Reddick, Papa Al was a dead man. Shortly after that, Papa Al disappeared from the scene — an example of the Haight's justice system in action.

Psychedelics in the '60s

In the early years of the clinic, Dr. Dave "exempted" psychedelic drugs from "drugs," such as methamphetamines. He believed then that psychedelics were "spiritual" and nonaddicting — *not* the view he holds today. The spiritual states induced by drugs can be attained by nonchemical means, he says now.

He used LSD on occasion; it was an important element in the whole counter-culture movement and important to him personally. He used the drug in controlled situations, often with a "guide" to help monitor the experience. He remembers one occasion with Alice when he sensed his soul or spirit had left his body, and he recalls floating above Alice as she cradled his head in her arms. That was a significant event for him, and today he believes in some form of afterlife because of that and other LSD experiences. He reflects somberly on how strange it is that a chemical could induce spiritual values far more meaningful to him than what resulted from the years of traditional religion he was exposed to when he was growing up in Bakersfield. He is convinced that LSD was one of the factors that changed and redirected him and that there wouldn't be a Haight Ashbury Free Medical Clinic if he hadn't experimented with it.

It's jarring to hear a world-famous expert on drug use and a founder of addiction medicine as a specialty within the American Medical Association say positive things about using an illegal drug. But Dave Smith is careful to put things into a historical and cultural context. He says that if you agree with many of the elements of the '60s, if you think founding the Haight Ashbury Free Medical Clinic was a good thing, if you appreciate the musical changes of those years — his older daughter, Julia, is named after John Lennon's "Julia," Lennon's mother's name — and if you appreciate the expanding art forms, then the role of psychedelic drugs must be acknowledged. For those times, he says, if you were a leader in the counter-culture revolution, then using LSD was almost mandatory.

Rick Seymour, one of Dave's close friends and collaborators, also took LSD and also has positive things to say about his experiences. Like Dave he now is completely drug and alcohol free and believes "spirituality" can be achieved without drugs. But he also links "psychedelic thinking" to the founding of the clinic. Psychedelic thinking, according to Rick, is "spiritually oriented, nonlinear, and nonmaterial." One becomes aware "of a basic unity in life between people and the world, that everything is in a sense connected, that there is a family of man." These values are strikingly different from those held by Dave Smith before 1966.

When the clinic began, all those involved believed in helping the hippies, who were basically good kids who had a vision of how culture and society could be improved. The doctors were not treating *addiction* in 1967; they were treating temporary and occasional bad effects from drugs and general health problems. But things changed rapidly, and after the Summer of Love the drug scene turned mean. Soon speed was rampant, then heroin, then cocaine, and by 1970 the clinic was having to deal with many aspects of addiction. A number of the medical volunteers who had started with the clinic became disillusioned, feeling that things had changed so much that drug use and its now often criminal context were beyond their means, and they quit and moved on.

Dave himself did a lot of soul-searching. He figured he either had to commit himself to the study of drug addiction as his professional specialty or close the clinic and move on as his colleagues had. He had earlier been interested in forensics medicine, and the notion of returning to that was appealing. He concluded, however, that studying and treating drug addiction was where he belonged, and he has been comfortable with that decision ever since.

Milestones

The early years of the clinic are chronicled in *Love Needs Care* by Dave Smith and John Luce (Little, Brown, 1968) and the later ones in *The Haight Ashbury Free Medical Clinics: Still Free After All These Years, 1967-1987* by Dave Smith and Richard B. Seymour (Partisan Press, 1986). Both give a fascinating look at the people and the times. Here are some milestones:

In 1974 Supervisor Dianne Feinstein was instrumental in getting the city to include the clinic in its health-care system, thus providing ongoing financial support. And about this time more and more grants began to come in, adding to the clinic's fiscal stability.

Later an internal problem surfaced and had to be dealt with. One of the doctors, a program manager within the clinic, lost control of his ego, according to Rick Seymour, and his autocratic manner led to dissension. The doctor in question thought Dave Smith was weak and could be toppled, Rick says, and he had always been envious of Dave's position and wished the clinic had been *his* idea. "It could have been an open battle that would have destroyed the clinic," Rick says.

Dave's style, according to Rick, "has not been to pound tables and take power back, but to work with people, have forbearance." So Dave developed a support system and worked diligently to solve the problem, to galvanize the staff and its programs. It worked, and the section head resigned.

In 1976 Dave attended the Democratic National Convention and met Jimmy Carter, who at that time was being advised by Dr. Peter Bourne about drug-related problems. Bourne had been a clinic volunteer during the clinic's early years. Dave visited Plains, Georgia, and met the Carter family, and Jimmy listened closely to Dave's views about drug policy and drug-treatment approaches. Jimmy's sister, Ruth Carter Stapleton, became a good friend and stayed at Dave's house when she visited later that year, which of course attracted a lot of media attention. Dave laughs, recalling the "Hippie Doctor and the President's Sister" being invited to a special luncheon at the UC medical center.

In February of 1977, Millicent Buxton joined the clinic on a work-study project for her B.A. in psychology from the University of San Francisco. Dave asked her to coordinate the proceedings of the 1977 National Drug Abuse Conference.

Millicent was in recovery from alcohol and heroin addiction, and she was appalled at some of the things she saw going on at the clinic. She didn't like the casual, hippie lifestyle, and she objected to the way the medical staff accepted the chronic addiction of their patients. More importantly, from her point of view, she couldn't see any evidence at all of *recovery* as part of the treatment programs. In other words, patients would wander in for help and undergo some form of detoxification, then be put back on the street, soon to return to repeat the process.

Millicent believed strongly in the 12-step self-help recovery program she was in, and she argued that the clinic should embrace some form of 12-step recovery as part of its treatment philosophy. She met with much resistance but she persevered, and today recovery is indeed part of the clinic's philosophy. Fifty-two 12-step meetings per week were held at the clinic in 1991, a statistic she reports with pride. Without question Millicent was a major force in getting both Dave and the clinic committed to the 12-step recovery process.

Toward the Mainstream

Addiction Medicine

*I*n 1970 Jess Bromley, an internist from San Leandro who was familiar with Dave Smith's work, called him in San Francisco and told him that two doctors in Southern California had been arrested for doing what Dave was doing every day, detoxing heroin addicts on an out-patient basis using prescription drugs such as Darvon and Valium.

At the time, addiction as a *disease* was used only in reference to alcoholics. Abusers of other drugs were criminal "dope fiends" in the language of the "establishment," and if they sought treatment they were seen by "dope docs." Dave and Jess decided they would have to work through mainstream channels to change the law so that treatment of drug addicts could continue, and they rallied support from their colleagues. In 1972 the two men founded the California Society of Addiction Medicine. Doctors in this specialty treat patients addicted to all psychoactive substances including alcohol, nicotine, prescription drugs, heroin, and cocaine.

With the strong support of the California Medical Association, Jess and Dave lobbied Sacramento and elicited endorsements from Assemblyman Bob Campbell and state Senator George Moscone. In 1974 the health and safety code was changed so that the kind of treatment Dave and the Southern California doctors were providing would be legal.

Later a new group, the California Society for the Treatment of Alcoholism and Other Drug Dependencies, was formed with Dave and Jess as prominent members and eventual presidents. The notion was to bring together doctors who treated alcoholics — addicts who had a socially acceptable disease — with those who treated addicts hooked on drugs that were not acceptable, creating a professional organization that addressed the whole spectrum of addiction.

These early efforts laid the foundation for the recognition of addiction medicine as a specialty and the formation of the American Society of Addiction Medicine. Dave and Jess have remained major players in this national organization.

In 1983 an exam for certification in addiction medicine was instituted, similar to the board certification given to primary specialties. In 1987, after careful groundwork by Dave and others, the American Medical Association passed a resolution stating that all forms of addiction are diseases, a major move in legitimizing the treatment of addiction. Dave Smith had believed from the beginning that being sick shouldn't be a crime, and the AMA action validated his belief.

Periodically the AMA sends doctors a census form asking them to identify their specialties by checking one of 24 primary ones, such as internal medicine, surgery, and obstetrics and gynecology; by checking one of about 100 self-designated specialties; or by checking "other." Anyone practicing addiction medicine before 1989 would have had to check "other."

But in 1989 something changed. Dave calls it "the most exciting moment in my mainstream medical career." At the AMA's annual convention, in response to work by delegate Jess Bromley and alternate delegate David Smith, the organization unanimously recognized addiction medicine as a self-designated specialty and gave it the symbol ADM. Now, when the census forms are sent, ADM is first on the self-designated list. The 24th primary specialty is emergency medicine, and Dave hopes that the 25th will be addiction medicine.

In 1992 David Smith is the board-nominated candidate for president-elect of the American Society of Addiction Medicine. He's come a long way from his early days on the fringe of the medical establishment. Jess Bromley states the obvious, that Dave is "held in great respect" and is "one of the foremost experts in the field widely sought as an expert witness and lecturer."

Dave admits he's proud of his achievements in giving addiction medicine the recognition it deserves.

He's proud, too, of the positive influence he's had on other doctors. He speaks of the "brilliant young Turks" who have come to the clinic since its beginning for exciting work free of major bureaucratic restraint.

Dr. John Luce, an internist at San Francisco General Hospital and a professor at the University of California Medical Center, met Dave in 1967 when John was a journalist. After receiving a B.A. in English from Stanford in 1963, John had worked for the Democratic Party in public relations until Reagan's election as governor in 1966. Switching to journalism, he wrote "A Young Doctor's Crusade" for *Look* in 1967. That article told the nation about what young Dr. Smith was undertaking in the Haight.

One unexpected outcome of the article was the cancellation of Dave's malpractice insurance. He received a call from his carrier's agent telling him that taking care of scores of hippies in a clinic setting was not what he had signed up to do. Panicking, Dave contacted the San Francisco Medical Society, and he is still grateful for the help the organization gave him in getting new insurance. In 25 years serving hundreds of thousands of patients, however, not one malpractice judgment has been filed against the clinic.

John Luce later became the clinic's first biographer, writing with Dave *Love Needs Care*. For the first time, John got to know a medical doctor who shared his strong social and political beliefs. He then enrolled at

San Francisco State to take courses he would need to prepare himself for medical school, wrote on the side, and was admitted to UC Medical Center in 1970. He says Dave Smith was a key person in influencing him to become a physician.

Recognition and Recovery

In the booklet published for East Bakersfield High School's 30th reunion in 1986, Dave Smith says he was "radicalized in the '60s, socialized in the '70s, and is now an aging hippie trying to mainstream in the '80s." From a professional standpoint, Dave certainly was moving to the mainstream as a leading spokesman for addiction medicine. But in some ways he was still back in the '60s, especially regarding his own use of drugs.

When the clinic first opened, many of the volunteer physicians believed that they would serve their drug-impaired patients better if they themselves experimented with the drugs that were being used on the streets at the time. Dave Smith agrees that this line of thinking sounds patently absurd now. But in the '60s there was a different mindset, he says, and clinic doctors doing dope was a reality.

Dave's last drunk was in 1966, and he prided himself in believing he had been in recovery for alcohol addiction ever since then. His friends remember him holding a beer or a glass of wine during the '70s, but he said this was essentially for show — to fit in. He said he would take a sip or two, and then when the time was right he would step out to his car and smoke a joint. Marijuana was his drug of choice, and he smoked it on occasion throughout the '70s and into the '80s.

When his relationship with Millicent Buxton began in the late '70s — they were married in the '80s — she found his continued use of marijuana troubling, and she was outspoken about it. She told Dave that he was fooling himself if he thought he really had been in recovery since 1966 when in fact he was continuing to use a drug. He followed the classic pattern of addiction and denied it.

Millicent kept urging him to wake up, telling him that she was beginning to notice some changes in behavior that indicated to her that his thinking was becoming impaired. Then one day she smelled marijuana in Dave's downstairs office in their home. She told Christopher, who confronted his father, saying, "Daddy, you broke the house rule — no drugs in our home." That was a very emotional moment for Dave Smith, and he soon made a commitment to the 12-step self-help recovery process, citing one of its guidelines: "Half-measures avail us nothing." This was for him a spiritual awakening similar to his LSD experience in the '60s.

Dave Smith is now completely drugfree and has been since the '80s. One of the major dimensions of his life today is his participation in an anonymous 12-step self-help recovery program. He attends several meetings a week, one of them made up almost exclusively of health-care professionals, and he believes that recovery programs such as his are *crucial* in keeping addicts in remission. There is no cure, he says, only remission. But he says firmly that 70 to 80 percent of addicts who receive good medical treatment and who join 12-step recovery programs will remain drugfree.

The 12 Steps

Such organizations as Narcotics Anonymous, Cocaine Anonymous, Al-Anon, Nar-Anon, Alateen, and Adult Children of Alcoholics all follow 12-step programs patterned after the one pioneered by Alcoholics Anonymous. To understand why the 12 steps are so effective, it's important to understand the spectrum of drug use: "Experimental use" is short-term drug use done socially, usually out of curiosity; "recreational use" is pretty much the same as experimental use but tends to be more patterned; "circumstantial use" is use related to coping with a specific problem — students using stimulants during finals week or long-distance truckers using them to extend endurance and alertness; "intensified use" is usually daily use as a way of achieving relief from a persistent problem or stressful situation; and "compulsive use" is highly intense use involving psychological dependence and often physical dependence as well.

These classifications, taken from *Drugfree: A Unique, Positive Approach to Staying Off Alcohol and Other Drugs* by Rick Seymour and David Smith (Facts on File Publications, 1987), do not include addiction. Rick and Dave believe that addiction isn't really a stage of drug use because it transcends all stages of use and abuse. They define addiction as "a disease entity with its own psychopathology characterized by compulsion, loss of control, and continued use in spite of adverse consequences." They believe it is progressive and potentially fatal if untreated — and incurable but remissable through abstinence and recovery.

Because of addiction's unique psychopathology, proponents of 12-step programs believe treatment must be multifaceted and thus far broader than the employment of a strict medical protocol.

The 12 Steps Based on Alcoholics Anonymous

1. We admitted we were powerless over alcohol, that our lives had become unmanageable.

2. Came to believe that a Power greater than ourselves could restore us to sanity.

3. Made a decision to turn our will and our lives over to the care of God *as we understood Him.*

4. Made a searching and fearless moral inventory of ourselves.

5. Admitted to God, to ourselves, and to another human being the exact nature of our wrongs.

6. Were entirely ready to have God remove all these defects of character.

7. Humbly asked Him to remove our shortcomings.

8. Made a list of all persons we had harmed, and became willing to made amends to them all.

9. Made direct amends to such people wherever possible, except when to do so would injure them or others.

10. Continued to take personal inventory and when we were wrong promptly admitted it.

11. Sought through prayer and meditation to improve our conscious contact with God *as we understood Him,* praying only for knowledge of His will for us and the power to carry that out.

12. Having had a spiritual awakening as the result of these steps, we tried to carry this message to alcoholics, and to practice these principles in all our affairs.

(The Twelve Steps are reprinted with permission of Alcoholics Anonymous World Services Inc. Permission to reprint this material does not mean that AA has reviewed or approved the content of this publication, nor that AA agrees with the views expressed herein. AA is a program of recovery

from alcoholism — use of the Twelve Steps in connection with programs and activities which are patterned after AA, but which address other problems, does not imply otherwise.)

Spirituality is highly evident in the 12 steps, but members are quick to point out that the phrase *God as we understood Him* is not an invitation to follow Christian fundamentalism, which some critics have alleged, but that it can be interpreted as a belief in some power in the universe greater than any individual. For Dave Smith, the spirituality he has found in his particular recovery program has replaced the spirituality he previously experienced using LSD and marijuana.

And this spirituality is very important to him. The month of January — the month in which his mother, father, and grandmother all died — has always brought with it depression and even thoughts of suicide. But since he's been following the 12 steps, each January has become easier, and January of 1992 was a stable and happy time for him.

As Dave reflects on his life and his recovery, he concludes that steps four and five have been especially important in enriching his life. He believes he is far more loving, open, and considerate than he was before he joined his recovery group, and he's happier and more content. He works hard to make and maintain good personal relationships, and his friends — especially those he's known since the '40s and '50s — are special to him. He admits, too, that he wouldn't have cooperated in having this story written before he committed himself to steps four and five. He gives strong credit to Millicent for helping him accept, both emotionally and intellectually, his 12-step recovery program.

Home in the Haight

Millicent says wryly that she didn't marry "the boy next door." It's not uncommon for Dave to be away for a week or more at a time, and during the academic year he's gone about half the time. Even when he's home his evenings are often occupied with meetings or tasks related to his work.

On the other hand, she and their son, Christopher, and stepdaughters Julia and Suzanne have had wonderful travel opportunities because of Dave's international lecture schedule. Millicent and Dave have dined at the White House, and Millicent has become friends with nationally prominent people such as Ruth Carter Stapleton and Betty Ford. But if she could have her way, Millicent says, she would like to have Dave at home more often.

Millicent is important to Dave's professional life as well as his family life. In 1980 she and Marty Jessup, who is a registered nurse and a clinical professor in nursing at the UC Medical Center, started the Bay Area Task Force for Impaired Nurses. This concept soon spread statewide, and today there are 33 groups that address the needs of addicted nurses, and their treatment has been accepted by the California Board of Registered Nurses.

Coretta Scott King and Dr. Dave at Glide Memorial Church, 1989

Photo by George T. Kruse

Seven of the nine A.V.S. members at Dave's 50th birthday party: Dave, Tom Alexander, Dennis DeWalt, Bill Thompson, Larry Baker, Clark Sturges, and Jim Hill

Betty Lin, Eddie Fisher, Dave, and Bill Graham at the clinic's 23rd anniversary party

Photo by Virginia Morgan

Friends from Bakersfield ready to celebrate the clinic's 25th anniversary

In addition to her association with Marty, since 1980 Millicent has been a partner with Dave in monitoring the recovery of other chemically dependent health professionals. She works for a group called Futures in Recovery, and often Dave joins her at her office to meet with their mutual patients.

Most recently, she and Dave are involved with principals, parents, and students, providing drug education in San Francisco schools. This began when several seventh and eighth graders in Christopher's school were found taking LSD.

Dave and Millicent rebut the notion that LSD is safe and nonaddicting, and they emphasize this to the parents and the kids. They point out, too, that at least three recent teenage suicides in the Bay Area were by youngsters who had a history of using LSD.

Many of the students they talk with are children of hippies who smoked dope and took LSD. It is becoming apparent that if the parents' use has stopped, the probability that their kids will use drugs is no different from children whose parents never used drugs. But if the parents are still using, then the probability that their children will use drugs is increased significantly. Dave and Millicent plan to continue their research on this.

Dave's home base for research and administration is an aging Victorian at 409 Clayton Street in the Haight, a building that has been part of the clinic since the beginning. Dave's office is on the third floor, the top one, located between the training and education section headed by Jeanne DiPrima, who also serves as Dave's administrative right hand, and a large room used as both a library and a counseling center.

It's a small, spartan office, almost professorial, not what you would expect the president of a multi-million-dollar corporation to occupy. But as Jeanne points out, for many years he didn't have an office at all — he just worked out of a bulging briefcase using any available chair or table. She was instrumental in clearing out the room and finding furniture for it.

Dave's office serves as a small historical museum. The walls are covered with awards, plaques, and certificates — Phi Beta Kappa, Who's Who in the United States, Addiction Medicine. Photographs show Dave with shoulder-length hair and love beads, Dave with sports teams from the clinics, with his friends Bill Graham, Eddie Fisher, Jerry Garcia, Chris Evert, the Rev. Cecil Williams; with Millicent and Julia, now 18, Suzanne, 17, and Christopher, 12.

He's a big man, standing 6 foot, 2 inches tall and weighing 200 pounds by a conservative guess. His curly brown hair is slightly long, but completely different from his pageboy of the '70s. When he lectures, consults, or teaches he usually wears a coat and tie. On other days he'll wear a polo shirt or turtleneck, often with a sport coat. Before he married Millicent he was a notoriously terrible dresser, known for mismatched outfits and colors that clashed, but now he generally makes a good appearance.

There are a variety of "typical" days for Dave Smith. The one he enjoys most is a family day, whether it's playing basketball with Christopher or going to shows or games with all the kids. He's a sports fanatic who holds 49ers and A's season tickets and is a careful follower of the Giants, Warriors, and Cal football. He's been to almost every Super Bowl in the past 10 years and would never miss a Big Game.

He began playing "A" class basketball at San Francisco's Olympic Club, then as the years passed "B," now "C," and he has a fantasy that the club will create a "D" class for him and other "aging hoopsters." During the final minutes of the 1991 "C" championship game, he saw a much younger opponent driving for the basket, and Dave moved in to check his lane. He turned his ankle stepping on the player's foot, heard his bone snap, and watched in pain and frustration as the go-ahead basket swished through the hoop.

Dave also likes to play tennis and golf but rarely finds time for either because of his frantic work and lecture schedule, which has taken him to Europe, Asia, and all 50 states. On vacation, though, he enjoys these sports and loves telling his golf partners, after shooting a round in the mid-80s, that the last time he played was six or eight months ago.

But few days, unfortunately, are family or sports days. A "typical" work day finds him rising early and working out on his Nordic exerciser while he watches CNN. Around 8 he leaves his family's beautifully restored 1898 Victorian and either walks three blocks to his Clayton Street office or drives to his other office on Crestmont Drive on Mount Sutro. About two or three times a week he meets there with Dave Newlin, whom he calls his business manager and financial consultant.

The two Daves have worked together since the mid-'60s. At that time Dave Smith wanted to invest in San Francisco real estate using the pension funds he inherited from his father, but he didn't have enough money to buy a building on his own. He decided to form what he called the San Francisco Real Estate Investment Club, but he needed advice about how to set all this up. His first advisor was fraternity brother Phil Newlin, but Phil didn't feel he had the doggedness to keep trying to talk Dave out of bad ideas. Phil thought his brother *would* have the persistence to do battle with Dave, who on occasion could be very bullheaded. The combination clicked.

Apart from their business relationship, Dave Newlin considers Dave Smith one of his closest friends, "almost a brother." He doesn't like to be called Dave's manager and consultant, but rather his investment administrator. He says he doesn't become involved in Dave's personal investments but rather oversees trusts, partnerships, leasing companies, etc. that are part of David E. Smith, M.D. Inc. Those assets essentially make up Dave Smith's pension fund.

Dave Newlin believes Dave Smith is a genius and a brilliant motivator "though not always good at groundwork." He says that Dr. Dave has a "complex mind" and that often people have trouble initially following his train of thought — but "if you stick with him long enough you'll see his consistency, even though it's not always clear at the outset." With Newlin's guidance

Dave Smith has become financially secure, achieving the goal his mother established for him when he was a schoolkid in Bakersfield.

On another "typical" work day Dave will be away lecturing, speaking on such topics as "The Disease Concept of Addiction," "Substance Abuse in the Workplace," "Proper Prescribing Practices," or "The Chemically Dependent Health Professional." While away he calls his office frequently, and each call creates new tasks for Jeanne DiPrima, who along with her work in training and education serves as his personal assistant. Dave still exhibits some of his old compulsiveness, and when an idea or question comes up he is quick to grab the phone, regardless of where he is or the time of day. Jeanne recalls that when she was on her last vacation she received 37 calls from Dave on her pager.

Rick Seymour has a telephone story, too. He remembers watching the end of a close 49er game and trying to ignore a ringing phone. Annoyed, he figured it was someone who wasn't a football fan, and he feared he would miss the finale. But it was Dr. Dave calling from somewhere over Detroit to ask about the game. When Rick told him it was close, Dave asked him to stay on the line and give him a play-by-play account, which Dave then relayed to the rest of the passengers on the plane.

Another work day might intersperse meetings around the Haight with quick visits back at 409 Clayton. According to Jeanne, "We see him for short periods of time in which there's a great flurry of activity that leaves a huge amount of work in its wake." Some of this work involves expert testimony in legal cases. In 1991 alone Dave received 85 requests and was retained in 75 cases, which makes him one of the leading medical-legal experts in the country on drug-related matters.

In one such case, Dave lectured an attentive Marin County murder trial jury about the effects of cocaine and alcohol on the brain. His presentation was very similar to one a professor would make to a bunch of undergrads in an introductory biology or psychology class. He drew a schematic of the brain on a flip chart, wrote out a spectrum of toxicity from 1 to 10 for both drugs, and explained that many abusers of cocaine also abuse alcohol to create a chemical balance (the depressant balances the stimulant) and that as a result the drug user can perform basic motor skills such as driving a car but generally exhibits poor judgment and has trouble with abstract thinking and broad explanations. At his conclusion the judge introduced his sketches as evidence. As Dave limped from the stand — he was wearing a walking cast because of his broken ankle — the judge gave him a second look and said, "Nice tie." Dave loved it.

Wednesdays for Dave mean driving across the bay to the MPI Treatment Services of Summit Medical Center in Oakland where he serves as research director. He supervises research studies and sees private patients, many of them health professionals with drug problems. A *perfect* work day for Dave would be a balance of treatment, teaching, and research, with a minimum of administration, which he likes the least.

Dave, Suzanne, Christopher, Millicent, Dominique DiPrima, and Julia at the clinic's 25th anniversary party

Dave holding *No Hiding Place* just signed by Cecil Williams

Michael Stepanian, chairman of the clinic's board of directors; Willie Brown, Speaker of the California Assembly; and Dave at the clinic's 25th anniversary party

Photo by Virginia Morgan

At 609 Clayton: Dave, Jeanne DiPrima, and Elizabeth Sullivan

Dave Newlin and Dr. Dave in their Crestmont office

Alice, Julia, Dave, and Suzanne in Sebastopol

Dave, Christopher, and Millicent at home in the Haight

Jeanne and Dave preparing for a trial

Rick Seymour and Dr. Dave

Much of the administration of Dave's professional life is handled by Jeanne DiPrima, who is the daughter of respected beat poet Diane DiPrima, and Elizabeth Sullivan, Dave's secretary. Liz firmly believes that Dave Smith will go to his grave carrying his cellular phone!

Jeanne has known Dave and Millicent since 1978, but she didn't begin working at the clinic until 1988. She started as Dave's secretary, and as her considerable talents became recognized she was promoted to director of training and education, where she turned a $23,000 deficit into a gain of $215,000. She monitors five different education and training grants, three from the government and two from private corporations. One of these has paid for the training of 1,467 nurses in one section at San Francisco General Hospital. In addition, Jeanne arranges and monitors the clinic's two annual conferences.

Since arriving at the clinic, she has raised Dave's legal and lecture fees and in many ways has become a personal manager for him regarding his consultancies. Jeanne, like Dave and Millicent, is in recovery, as are almost half of the other 200 paid staff members at the clinic. She says Dave likes to hire people in recovery because he believes "the 12-step process allows people to grow and adds a level of communication and intimacy to the work environment." She believes that Dave's work at the clinic fulfills his spiritual need, and that his other tasks, which add significantly to his income, allow him to support his family as he wants to. While his fees are high, he donates approximately one-third of this money to the clinic.

Jeanne also handles the frequent requests that come in from the media. Whenever anything happens that involves drugs — from a new epidemic to the drug-related death of a celebrity — Dave Smith is contacted first. Jeanne estimates that she receives about 50 calls a year from NBC Nightly News, and she's on a first-name basis with Ted Koppel and his ABC Nightline staff.

She considers Dave Smith brilliant, generous, and dedicated, but she does wish he would get rid of his "wolves-at-the-door" mentality and spend more money on office space, equipment, and staff. She repeats the old axiom that "it takes money to make money." She acknowledges, though, that given Dave's Bakersfield blue-collar roots he's probably not going to change.

A Pinnacle

A gala at the Fairmont Hotel on June 6, 1992, celebrated the clinic's 25th anniversary. Eddie Fisher was the star performer, and he thanked Dave Smith for his help in monitoring his own recovery from drug and alcohol addiction and for being an attentive and caring friend.

The Fairmont's Grand Ballroom was packed with civic leaders, clinic employees and supporters, and many of Dave's other friends. Assembly Speaker Willie Brown, a longtime supporter of the clinic, described some of the clinic's accomplishments and spoke warmly of its founder and president. Later in the evening Dave displayed plaques from Mayor Frank Jordan of San Francisco, Mayor Elihu Harris of Oakland, and Mayor George Livingston of Richmond, all citing the role the clinic has played in the medical and social network of the Bay Area.

San Francisco Supervisor Willie Kennedy and Health Commissioner Naomi Gray were part of the celebration, and Dominique DiPrima, a San Francisco television personality who has won five Emmys for her show "Home Turf," was M.C. Jeanne DiPrima is Dominique's sister.

Millicent, Julia, Suzanne, and Christopher were with Dave at his table. Next to them were two tables of friends from Bakersfield, 14 of whom had attended East Bakersfield High School with Dave. At a nearby table was Jennifer Ellis McIntosh, Dave's fiancee from the early '60s, who had flown in from Southern California.

A few weeks after the anniversary gala, Dave and Jess Bromley represented the American Society of Addiction Medicine at the annual AMA meeting in Chicago. They were instrumental in passing a resolution requiring corporate medical officers to be informed about addiction as a disease, and they proposed a guideline to specify that addicted health-care professionals in well-monitored recovery programs should be allowed to practice. At about this same time, Gov. Bill Clinton in proposing his universal health plan said, "Health care is a right, not a privilege," Dave's slogan from 1967, which then had seemed so radical.

Dave believes the management of the clinic has never been better, and he gives credit for this to Herb Houston, CEO since April 1987. At that time, according to Dave, the clinic was a white, hippie community out of step with the times — a social dinosaur. Herb Houston, an African American with an M.A. in health administration from the University of Southern California and with extensive experience managing public agencies, took charge. He began a complete administrative reorganization by standardizing policies, updating documents, networking with the external community, establishing a quality assurance committee, and introducing a team approach to problem solving. Included in all of this was the goal of hiring more members of minority groups. And that goal has been reached. Dave says the clinic is now a model minority community-action social-service agency.

Herb sees the clinic expanding to more sites in Northern California — the Bill Graham Center for Health and Recovery opened in October — and says that in five years it will be "right in the mix" helping to serve the 3 to 5 million Californians without any kind of health insurance. He attributes the success of the clinic to Dave Smith's vision.

Dave's close friend, the Rev. Cecil Williams of Glide Memorial Church, also speaks of this vision. He calls Dave "a man of his time" who is solid, grounded, a man who knows what he wants. The two have worked for years on a variety of social issues. He married Dave and Millicent in their home in the Haight and also christened Christopher there. Cecil's wife, Janice Mirikitani, is one of Millicent's best friends.

What does the future hold? Dave Smith says he wants "to grow and develop within the framework of what I have in the Haight Ashbury." He doesn't want any major changes and would like to travel less so he could have more time with Millicent and the kids, but he understands that he has to keep earning a living and advancing addiction medicine, and that teaching and lecturing is part of that life. He hopes, though, that future years will show a bit more stability.

It's November 1992, late in the afternoon on the third floor of 409 Clayton, and Dave Smith is in a reflective mood. Looking back, he is proud of two accomplishments: establishing the clinic and pioneering addiction medicine. He regrets that his parents didn't have the chance to know him as an adult and to see the things he's done, but he's adjusted to the reality and knows that Dorothy would indeed be proud of him. She "inspired and pushed me," he says, and he loves her and appreciates all she did for him. He is no longer ashamed of his background, he's proud of it, and he gives credit to his recovery program for much of the inner peace he now enjoys. He has achieved the goals he established for himself as a boy in Bakersfield, but he took a route far different from what he had initially envisioned.

Leaning forward in his chair, he says that in 1967 he thought a conversation 25 years later would go something like this: "Dr. Smith, I was looking through some old copies of the *Chronicle,* and I came across some articles about a hippie clinic of some sort back in the '60s. Can you tell me what went on there and whatever happened to it?"

That hippie clinic has become an institution. It has met the medical and social needs of more than a million people, and its founder is confident that it will continue to grow and serve millions more. For now, though, he looks at his watch, remembers it's time to pick up Christopher at school, packs his briefcase, hugs Jeanne and tells her he'll call her later that night or first thing in the morning, and heads down the stairs out onto the street.

Walking toward his car, past the medical building at the corner of Clayton and Haight with blue and white banners flying to signal its 25th anniversary, he notices a young girl with her hand outstretched. He gives her all the change from his pocket and smiles as she says shyly, "Thanks, Dr. Dave."